what would you ask?
THOMAS EDISON

Anita Ganeri
Illustrated by Nick Spender

Belitha Press

First published in the UK in 2000 by
Belitha Press Limited, London House,
Great Eastern Wharf, Parkgate Road,
London SW11 4NQ

ISBN 1 84138 136 5

British Library Cataloguing in Publication Data
for this book is available from the British Library.

Printed in Singapore

10 9 8 7 6 5 4 3 2 1

Editor: Veronica Ross
Designer: Caroline Grimshaw
Illustrator: Nick Spender
Consultants: Hester Collicutt and Alison Porter

Contents

What do you do?

'I am an inventor. I invented the phonograph and the electric light bulb.'

Before light bulbs were invented, people used candles and later gaslights or oil lamps to light up their homes. These were fiddly to light and were not very bright. Today, all you have to do is go into a room and press a switch to turn the lights on. What could be easier?

The electric light bulb was invented about 120 years ago by American inventor, Thomas Edison. In 1879, after almost a year's hard work, he succeeded in making a light bulb that burned brightly for an amazing 13 hours. His invention quickly caught on. Edison also invented a way of making electricity and supplying it to people's homes.

Although Edison is famous for the light bulb, this was not his only invention. Throughout his long career, he applied for more than a thousand patents. They included a talking doll, the earliest record player and an early type of movie camera. Today, Edison is remembered as one of the greatest inventors that ever lived.

Where were you born?

'I was born in Ohio, USA.'

Thomas Edison was born on
11 February 1847 in the little town
of Milan, Ohio, USA. His middle
name was Alva and his family
always called him 'Al'. His parents,
Samuel and Nancy, had seven
children altogether. But three of
them died when they were young.
Thomas was the youngest child.
By the time he was born, his brothers
and sisters were already teenagers.

Thomas' father owned a timber business. But the business failed and, in 1854, Thomas and his family moved to a house near Port Huron in Michigan. Thomas was seven years old. Samuel got a job as a carpenter and lighthouse keeper at the local army base.

At about this time, Thomas caught scarlet fever which left him hard of hearing. His hearing grew worse and worse as he got older.

Were you good at school?

'I only went to school for three months. After that my mother taught me.'

Not long after moving to Port Huron, Thomas was sent to the local school. He only stayed for a few months. Thomas was a clever and curious boy. But his poor hearing and way of asking questions soon got him into trouble. He found lessons boring and was always bottom of the class. One day, he overheard his teacher saying that something must be wrong with him. Furious, Thomas ran out of the schoolhouse and never went back.

Thomas' mother, Nancy, had trained as a teacher and she decided to teach her son at home. Thomas especially loved reading. When he was nine, he read a book about how to do simple science experiments. He set up a laboratory in the basement at home and started doing his own experiments.

What was your first job?

'It was selling newspapers on the trains.'

In 1859, when Thomas was 12 years old, the railway came to town. The Grand Trunk Railroad opened a new line from Port Huron to Detroit. Young Thomas left his schooldays behind and found himself a job. He worked as a newsboy, selling newspapers on the trains. Soon he was making a bit of extra money by selling sweets and refreshments as well.

Thomas' day began at dawn when he caught the morning train to Detroit. He returned home to Port Huron at half past nine at night. Between each daily run, he spent his spare time reading books in the Detroit library. He said later that this was the happiest time of his life. He spent his wages on science books and set up a laboratory in a spare wagon on the train so that he could get on with his hobby.

What did you do after that?

'I worked as a telegraph operator.'

The electric telegraph was invented in 1844 by American, Samuel Morse. Morse code is a series of dots and dashes. The telegraph sent this code as a series of electrical pulses along the wire, heard as beeps at the receiving end. The operator receiving the message learned how to understand the code and translate it back into words. For the first time, people could send long-distance messages quickly and easily.

Thomas was fascinated by the telegraph. He even set up his own telegraph at home. Then, in 1862, aged 16, he became a telegraph operator. His first job was in the telegraph office at Port Huron. Afterwards, he spent six years as a 'tramp telegrapher'. He went from place to place working for whoever paid the highest wages.

Thomas liked to work the night shift to leave the day free for science. But his experiments often got him into trouble. He even blew one telegraph office up. He never kept a job for very long!

How did you become an inventor?

'I read a book by a famous scientist called Michael Faraday.'

In 1868, Thomas moved to the city of Boston. At that time, many of America's best scientists and inventors lived there. With the money he earned from his job at the Western Union Telegraph Company, Thomas bought a book called *Experimental Researches in Electricity* by the English scientist, Michael Faraday. It made him want to become an inventor more than ever.

A few months later, Thomas left his job. He wanted more time for experiments. In 1869 he was granted a patent for his first invention, an automatic electrical vote counter for use in the US government. Unfortunately, nobody wanted to buy it. He had better luck with his next invention. It was a machine called a stock ticker, based on the telegraph. It was used in the Stock Exchange to send the latest stock prices from office to office.

With the money Thomas earned from the stock ticker, he set up a workshop in a factory in Newark, New Jersey. And in 1871, he married Mary Stilwell, a worker at the factory.

Where did you work?

'I set up an inventions factory at Menlo Park in New Jersey.'

Five years later, in 1876, Thomas moved again. He bought some land in a village called Menlo Park and built a large, new workshop and a laboratory. He called it an 'inventions factory'. He wanted it to be a place especially for devising and making inventions.

To help bring his ideas to life, Thomas hired a team of scientists, engineers and workers. He worked incredibly hard, sometimes going without sleep for days on end. And he expected his workers to do the same. Once he locked them in and would not let them leave until the job was finished!

In 1877 Thomas came up with the idea for one of his most famous inventions. He designed a machine, called a phonograph, for recording the sound of the human voice. (Today we would call it a record player.) This had never been done before. The first recording was the popular nursery rhyme, 'Mary had a little lamb'.

What was your greatest invention?

'After the phonograph,
it was the electric light bulb.'

In the 1870s, most homes were lit by
gaslights or oil lamps. The only electric
lights were called arc lights, but these
were big and glaring, and gave off
harmful fumes. Thomas wanted
to invent a light that would be
cheap, easy and safe to use.
He called it a 'glow bulb'.

Thomas announced that the glow bulb would take him six weeks to invent. In fact, it took over a year. The idea was to put a filament inside a small, glass globe. When the light was switched on, electricity would make the filament glow. But what should he make the filament from? Thomas tried many different materials, including gold, fishing line and coconut fibre. Finally, in October 1879, a glow bulb made with a cotton thread filament burned for over 13 hours. On New Year's Eve, Menlo Park was lit up with strings of the new light bulbs.

Did it change your life?

'Yes. It made me rich and famous!'

Thomas wanted to see light bulbs in every home, office and factory, but there was a problem. First, there had to be a system for making electricity and supplying it to people. So Thomas invented one. In September 1882, the Pearl Street power station in New York opened. It was the first of its kind in the world.

The electricity business boomed. Thomas set up his own electric light companies in the USA and Europe. It made him a very rich man. But Thomas was bad at managing his money. It was always running out!

The phonograph and the light bulb made sure that Thomas' name was known all over the world. He became friends with famous scientists, leaders and businessmen. In the USA, he was nicknamed 'the Wizard' and treated like a hero. But, in 1884, tragedy struck. His wife, Mary, died of typhoid.

Did you invent anything else?

'I invented lots of things, including an early type of movie camera.'

Two years after Mary's death, Thomas married again. His new wife's name was Mina Miller. She tried to make him work shorter hours and spend more with his family. But she did not succeed! In 1887, Thomas moved to a new inventions factory at West Orange, New Jersey. It was ten times bigger than Menlo Park!

Hundreds more inventions followed, including talking dolls with tiny phonographs inside them that played nursery rhymes. Thomas also invented two machines called a kinetograph and a kinetoscope. The kinetograph was an early type of movie camera. The kinetoscope was used for viewing the finished film.

Not all of Thomas'
inventions were
successful. He lost
a fortune on a mining
project. Another idea for
building cheap, concrete
houses, complete with
concrete furniture, never
caught on. But Thomas
did not give up. His wife
said that he was always
inventing something,
even in his dreams.

When did you retire?

'I never really retired. I always worked hard.'

Thomas worked long hours all his life. He believed that 'genius is one per cent inspiration, ninety-nine per cent perspiration'. He often worked all night and slept all day. Sometimes he did not bother going to bed. He just fell asleep on top of his desk.

Despite the long hours spent in his laboratory, Thomas had always been fit and healthy. But in 1929, after attending a celebration marking the 50-year anniversary of electric light, his health began to fail. Thomas Edison died on 18 October 1931. He was 84 years old. He was buried three days later on a hillside near his West Orange laboratory. That evening, all over America, people showed their respects by turning off their lights for one minute.

How is Thomas Edison remembered today?

In all, Thomas Edison took out 1,093 patents, which is still a world record for any inventor. The 'Wizard' was always bursting with good ideas. The phonograph, an early type of movie camera and projector, artificial rubber, waxed paper, are just some of his inventions.

Thomas Edison is best remembered for the invention of the light bulb and his work on electricity. Both of these things are so important that it is hard to imagine life without them.

From the time of his difficult childhood in Port Huron, Thomas Alva Edison went on to become one of the greatest inventors there has ever been. Despite the fact that he hardly went to school, he earned fame and fortune through sheer hard work, and succeeded in changing the world.

Some important dates

1847 Thomas Alva Edison is born in Milan, Ohio, USA.

1854 The Edison family move to Port Huron, Michigan. Thomas catches scarlet fever. This may have caused his later deafness.

1855 Thomas goes to school for three months. Afterwards his mother teaches him at home.

1859 Thomas becomes a newspaper boy on the railway.

1863 Thomas becomes a telegraph operator. He is called a 'tramp operator' because he moves from place to place for work.

1868 Thomas moves to Boston. He gets a job at the Western Union Telegraph Company. He starts inventing. He applies for his first patent for his electrical vote counter.

1869 Thomas applies for his second patent for a stock ticker. He moves to New York and sets up in business with telegraph engineer, Franklin L Pope.

1871 Thomas sets up a workshop in Newark, New Jersey. On Christmas Day, he marries Mary Stilwell.

1876 Edison moves his workshop to Menlo Park. He calls it his 'inventions factory'.

1877 Thomas starts work on improving the newly-invented telephone. In December, he invents the phonograph and makes and plays back the first sound recording.

1878 Thomas starts works on the electric light and on developing a public electricity supply.

1879 In October Thomas succeeds in making an electric light bulb which burns for 13 hours. In Britain, inventor Joseph Swan also works on designing a light bulb.

1881 Thomas leaves Menlo Park and moves back to New York.

1884 Thomas' wife, Mary, dies.

1886 Thomas marries his second wife, Mina Miller. They set up home in West Orange, New Jersey where Thomas builds a new workshop and laboratory.

1888 Thomas experiments with mining techniques for processing iron ore. The project is a costly failure.

1891 Thomas patents the kinetoscope in the USA.

1912 Thomas starts work on improvements for the Model-T Ford automobile. He becomes great friends with Henry Ford.

1914-1918 During World War I, Thomas works on scientific projects for the US Navy. He develops a torpedo-detector, an underwater telephone and an anti-submarine device.

1927 Thomas experiments with making synthetic rubber.

1929 Thomas attends a 50-year anniversary celebration of electric light. His Menlo Park laboratory is rebuilt in the Museum of History.

1931 Thomas becomes ill and dies on 18 October. He is 84 years old. To honour him, many lights are switched off in the USA.

Glossary

artificial Something which is not natural or naturally made.

automatic Something which happens by itself, on its own.

code A way of sending messages using signs and symbols to stand for words and letters.

concrete A very hard material used for building.

devise To invent or plan out.

Michael Faraday A famous British scientist who lived from 1791-1810. His pioneering work in physics and chemistry and his discoveries about electricity and magnetism are still vitally important today.

filament A long, thin thread or part, such as the thin piece of wire that glows inside an electric light bulb.

fumes Smoke or vapours which can be smelly or even poisonous.

laboratory A room or building used by a scientist or inventor for carrying out experiments.

Morse Code A code of dots and dashes invented by American Samuel Morse in the 1840s for use on the telegraph system. Different combinations of dots and dashes stand for different letters and numbers.

ore A type of rock in which different metals are found. For example, iron is found in iron ore.

patent An official document that is awarded to inventors. It states that a person is the rightful inventor of an item and gives him or her the rights to their invention for a set number of years.

phonograph A machine invented by Edison for recording the sound of the human voice, something which had never been done before.

power station A factory-like building where electricity is produced from coal, gas, oil or nuclear power.

projector A machine for projecting, or showing, a picture on a screen.

scarlet fever A highly contagious (easily caught) disease which gives sufferers a fever and a rash all over the body.

Stock Exchange An organization that trades in stocks and shares. People buy shares, or part ownership in companies, in the hope of making a profit if the company does well and the shares go up in price.

stock ticker A machine invented by Edison for sending the prices of stocks and shares between the different Stock Exchange offices.

telegraph A machine that sends letters and words along a wire or wires, in the form of an electrical code.

tramp telegrapher A telegraph operator who travelled from place to place, working for different telegraph offices.

typhoid A very dangerous disease which is marked by high fever, headaches, a red rash and a muddled mind.

vote counter A machine invented by Edison for automatically counting the votes cast in government elections.

Index